Get read-y for the KS1 SATs with CGP!

The short, sharp tests in this book are a brilliant way to help pupils prepare for the KS1 SATs Reading Test in 2017 and beyond.

They're just like mini versions of the real SATs, including reading texts that become more challenging throughout the set.

Plus — all the answers are included in a cut-out-and-keep section!

What CGP is all about

Our sole aim here at CGP is to produce the highest quality books — carefully written, immaculately presented and dangerously close to being funny.

Then we work our socks off to get them out to you — at the cheapest possible prices.

Contents

Set C

Published by CGP

Editors: Charlotte Burrows, Emma Crighton, Alex Fairer, Cathy Lear, Louise McEvoy
Contributors: Amanda MacNaughton, John Svatins
With thanks to Alison Griffin and Glenn Rogers for the proofreading.
With thanks to Laura Jakubowski for the copyright research.

Contains public sector information licensed under the Open Government Licence v3.0
http://www.nationalarchives.gov.uk/doc/open-government-licence/version/3/

ISBN: 978 1 78294 707 3
Clipart from Corel®
Printed by Elanders Ltd, Newcastle upon Tyne.
Based on the classic CGP style created by Richard Parsons.

There are **5 questions**.
Give yourself **10 minutes** to read the text and answer them.

Tibbles Goes Missing

Aditi was worried. Her cat Tibbles hadn't been at home when she returned from school and no one had seen her all day.

"Don't worry," said Dad. "Cats like to explore. She'll come back."

The next day was Saturday. Tibbles still hadn't come back, so Aditi decided to act. She printed out photos of Tibbles and used them to make posters. On each one she wrote, 'Have you seen this cat? We miss her. If you see her, please call in at 32 Beech Road.'

That afternoon, Mum and Aditi went out and put up the posters all over town. There was still no sign of Tibbles. Aditi was miserable — what if they never saw her again? As they were walking home, they passed a man and a little girl looking at one of Aditi's posters.

"Look Daddy," said the little girl, pointing at the poster, "it's Fluffy."

The man said that Fluffy was a cat who often visited their house. "She looks the same as the cat in this photo. She might be in our garden now."

They all walked to the man's house. As they went into the garden, they saw that the man had been right. There was Tibbles, asleep on the lawn! Aditi grinned and ran to her. Tibbles jumped into Aditi's arms and purred happily. Aditi was very glad to have her back.

1. How did Aditi feel about the fact Tibbles was missing?

....

2. Why did Aditi print out photos of Tibbles?

....

3. Aditi and Mum went out to...

Tick **one** box.

get some photos printed. ☐

put up Aditi's posters. ☐

fetch Tibbles from the vet. ☐

go to Aditi's school. ☐

4. Number these events in the order in which they happened in the story.

   The first one has been done for you.

   Mum and Aditi put up some posters.   [ ]

   Aditi's cat went missing.   [1]

   The man thought he knew where Tibbles was.   [ ]

   Mum and Aditi went to the man's house.   [ ]

1 mark

5. How can you tell that Tibbles was pleased to see Aditi? Give **two** ways.

   1) ....

   2) ....

2 marks

END OF TEST

/ 6

There are **5 questions**.
Give yourself **10 minutes** to read the text and answer them.

Planning a Birthday Party

Birthday parties can be a fun chance for family and
friends to have a good time together. Here are a few tips
to help you if you're going to have a party of your own.

Inviting guests

Firstly, think about the kind of party you would like. Do you want a
small party with your closest friends, or a larger one with your whole
class? Be sure to talk about it with your parents before you decide.

Where to have your party

When you've chosen who to invite, you can decide where to have the
party. For a small party, you could invite people to your house. Large
parties will probably need to be held somewhere bigger. Restaurants
can be good as they provide tasty food. If you want to play games or
have a disco, village halls are a great choice.

Things to do

It's a good idea to organise activities for your guests, especially if
you're having your party at home. Games such as musical statues
or pass the parcel will keep your guests entertained. Make sure you
have lots of prizes so everyone gets a chance to win.

Have a great time!

1.   What is the text about?

Tick **one** box.

leaving a birthday party ☐

going to a birthday party ☐

planning a birthday party ☐

clearing up after a birthday party ☐

_____
1 mark

2.   Look at the section called *Inviting guests*

Find and **copy one** word that means the same as *choose*.

....
_____
1 mark

3.   Who might you invite to a small party?

....
_____
1 mark

4. Number these instructions in the order in which they appear in the text.

The first one has been done for you.

Choose how many people to invite. `1`

Organise activities for your guests. ☐

Make sure you have lots of prizes. ☐

Choose where you will have the party. ☐

1 mark

5. Tick each row to show whether each statement about birthday parties is **true** or **false**.

Statement	True	False
Large parties should be held in a small place.		
Restaurants don't provide any food.		
Activities will entertain your guests.		
Birthday parties can be fun for family and friends.		

2 marks

END OF TEST

/ 6

There are **5 questions**.
Give yourself **10 minutes** to read the text and answer them.

The Hidden Chest

Captain Billhook was very angry. His crew had been digging on the island for four hours, but there was still no sign of his treasure.

Nothing was going to plan. There had been four of them at first, but only Captain Billhook and Lucky Bob remained. Scallywag Sid had fallen into a pit and was still trying to get out. Fearless Fabio had been chased up a tree by a bear and refused to come down. Lucky Bob was the only one still digging.

"I can't find the treasure, Captain Billhook," called Lucky Bob, wiping the sweat from his forehead. "What did you say it was buried in?"

"It's in a wooden chest. Hurry up! I'll get sunburnt if I have to stay out here for much longer," replied the captain. Lucky Bob glared at him, but he kept digging.

Clunk. Lucky Bob's spade hit something. Captain Billhook jumped quickly into the hole. He pushed Lucky Bob aside and opened the chest. Laughing, he stared at the jewels inside — then everything went black and he fell to the ground.

It was dark when Captain Billhook woke up. Next to him was a note. *'Sorry for hitting you, but I'm fed up with being a pirate. I've taken the treasure to buy myself a house far from the sea. Lucky Bob.'*

1. Why did Scallywag Sid have to stop
   searching for treasure?

   ....

2. What did Captain Billhook think would happen
   to him if he had to stay outside for too long?

   ....

3. *Laughing, he stared at the jewels...*

   What does the word *stared* mean in this sentence?

   Tick **one** box.

   smiled   ☐

   looked   ☐

   jumped   ☐

   grabbed   ☐

4. How can you tell that Captain Billhook was keen to look at the treasure? Give **two** ways.

   1) ....

   2) ....

2 marks

5. Number these events in the order in which they happened in the story.

   The first one has been done for you.

   Lucky Bob left Captain Billhook a note. ☐

   Fearless Fabio was chased up a tree. 1

   Lucky Bob hit Captain Billhook. ☐

   Lucky Bob found the treasure. ☐

1 mark

END OF TEST

/ 6

There are **5 questions**.
Give yourself **10 minutes** to read the text and answer them.

A Lesson Learnt?

"I've only been horse riding a few times, but I'm very good at it," boasted Felix's cousin Martin as they waited for their lesson to start. Felix groaned. Martin, who was staying with him for a week, was constantly trying to prove that he was the best at everything.

Sharon, Felix's riding instructor, took them over to meet the two ponies she'd selected for them. After helping Felix onto Beth, his usual pony, she turned to help Martin onto Shelly.

"I can't ride this pony. It's too small," Martin lied. "The one I usually ride is that size." He pointed to Rufus, a much larger pony.

Sharon looked surprised, but led Rufus over and helped Martin onto his back. Martin swallowed nervously and gripped the reins tightly.

When Sharon and Felix moved off, Martin tried to follow. But Rufus tossed his glossy head and refused to walk forward. Martin shook the reins and shouted, but nothing he did could make Rufus move.

"Sorry, Martin, Rufus doesn't want to ride today. You'll have to ride Shelly instead," said Sharon. Martin scowled, but he let Sharon help him onto Shelly.

As the lesson began again, Martin realised he felt much better riding a smaller horse. Shelly was far easier to ride than Rufus had been. By the end of the lesson, he couldn't wait to go horse riding again.

1. How long was Martin staying with Felix for?

   ....

   1 mark

2. Draw lines to match each character
   to the correct description.

Character	Description
Sharon	the riding instructor
Martin	the pony that Felix rode
Beth	Felix's cousin

   1 mark

3. Why did Martin want to ride Rufus?

   Tick **one** box.

   Martin was scared of the other ponies. ☐

   Rufus was very friendly. ☐

   Martin had ridden Rufus before. ☐

   Martin wanted to ride a bigger pony. ☐

   1 mark

4.   What did Rufus refuse to do?

....

5.   a) Think about the story you have just read.
          If Martin had another riding lesson, how do you think
          he would act differently?

....

      b) How can you tell?

....

....

END OF TEST

/ 6

There are **5 questions**.
Give yourself **10 minutes** to read the text and answer them.

Hang-Gliding

Have you ever dreamt of soaring high above the ground like a bird? Well, people who practise the sport of hang-gliding can do just that. Like birds, they don't need an engine to help them fly.

What is a hang-glider?

Hang-gliders look a bit like large paper aeroplanes. Their wings are made of strong fabric, which copes well in wind and rain. The pilot lies in a harness below the wings.

Flight

Pilots control hang-gliders using their bodies. To steer, pilots tilt their bodies left or right. They can adjust their speed by leaning backwards or forwards. Hang-gliders can remain in the air for hours. The longest distance ever flown by a hang-glider without stopping is over 450 miles!

The hang-gliding experience

Many people find the hang-gliding experience amazing. Hang-gliders have a perfect view of the world below them. Although flying in heavy rain or strong winds can sometimes be risky, hang-gliding is usually very safe. Many people who hang-glide even find it peaceful. "I always feel calmer after a glide," one experienced pilot said. "Hang-gliding is my way of relaxing and getting outdoors."

1. What are hang-glider wings made of?

    ....
                                                                    _____
                                                                    1 mark

2. How do pilots steer hang-gliders?

                                    Tick **one** box.

         by leaning forwards   ☐
         by turning a wheel   ☐
         by leaning backwards   ☐
         by tilting their bodies   ☐

                                                                    _____
                                                                    1 mark

3. Look at the section called *The hang-gliding experience.*

    Find and **copy one** word that means
    the same as *dangerous*.

    ....
                                                                    _____
                                                                    1 mark

4. Why do many people find hang-gliding amazing?

....

....

1 mark

5. Tick each row to show whether each statement about
    hang-gliders is **true** or **false**.

Statement	True	False
The longest flight ever is 45 miles.		
They have no engines.		
They are controlled by their pilots.		
They are made out of paper.		

2 marks

END OF TEST

/ 6

There are **6 questions**.
Give yourself **10 minutes** to read the text and answer them.

The Kind Moon

I think the moon is very kind
To take such trouble just for me.
He came along with me from home
To keep me company.

He went as fast as I could run;
I wonder how he crossed the sky?
I'm sure he hasn't legs and feet
Or any wings to fly.

Yet here he is above their roof;
Perhaps he thinks it isn't right
For me to go so far alone,
Tho'* mother said I might.

by Sara Teasdale

*Tho' = though

17   **Set A**: Test 6

1. What does the child in the poem think of the moon?

Tick **one** box.

it's caring ☐

it's lonely ☐

it's angry ☐

it's sad ☐

1 mark

2. **Find** and **copy one** word from the text which means a place where someone lives.

....

1 mark

3. The child thinks that the moon is moving...

Tick **one** box.

faster than the child can run. ☐

further away from the child. ☐

at the same speed as the child. ☐

closer to the child. ☐

1 mark

4. Write down **two** things that the child in the poem is sure the moon doesn't have.

1) ....

2) ....

5. At the end of the poem, where is the moon?

Tick **one** box.

above a roof ☐

over the sea ☐

over the horizon ☐

behind a hill ☐

6. What does the child think the moon is doing?

Tick **one** box.

following the child ☐

talking to the child's mother ☐

sitting under the child's roof ☐

visiting the child's house ☐

END OF TEST

/ 6

End of Set A: Scoresheet

You've finished a full set of tests — well done!

Put your scores in here
to see how you're doing...

	Score	
Test 1		/6
Test 2		/6
Test 3		/6
Test 4		/6
Test 5		/6
Test 6		/6
Total		**/36**

... then look up your total score to see what's next:

0 – 12	You might need some **more practice**. Ask an adult to help, then try the tests again.
13 – 24	**Read** back over your **wrong** answers to see **why** they were wrong. Then try the **next set** of tests.
25 – 36	Well done! Try to beat your score on the **next set** of tests.

But first... bend your brain round this:

Rearrange the letters below to make an animal...

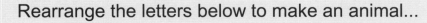

E   A   S   K   N   _ _ _ _ _

There are **5 questions**.
Give yourself **10 minutes** to read the text and answer them.

Rock Pools

Rock pools are found at the seaside. They are pools of seawater that get left behind when the tide goes out. These pools are usually surrounded by rocks that stop the water from trickling away.

Amazing animals

Lots of different animals live in rock pools. Crabs, small fish and sea slugs are just a few of the creatures that you might discover if you look closely. If you're really lucky, there might even be a starfish. Just be careful not to disturb any animals as you look around!

A difficult place to live

The animals that live in rock pools have to be tough. The water can get very hot or very cold. Sometimes, waves crash against the rocks. Lots of creatures can stick themselves to the rocks. This stops them from getting washed away by the waves.

Leaving the rock pool

When the tide comes in, the sea covers the rock pools and hides them from view. Many animals leave their rock pools when the tide comes in to explore and find food. Small fish usually return to their rock pools before the sea goes back out. Some of them live in the same rock pool for their whole lives.

1. Where are rock pools found?

Tick **one** box.

on top of cliffs ☐

by the sea ☐

underground ☐

next to lakes ☐

_____
1 mark

2. Look at the section called *Amazing animals*.

   Find and **copy one** word that means the same as *find*.

   ....

_____
1 mark

3. Why do some creatures stick themselves to rocks?

Tick **one** box.

so they don't get washed away ☐

so they can stay warm ☐

so they can grow bigger ☐

so they can find food ☐

_____
1 mark

4. What hides rock pools when the tide comes in?

....

5. Tick each row to show whether each statement about rock pools is **true** or **false**.

Statement	True	False
Not many different animals live in rock pools.		
Rock pools are filled with seawater.		
Some small fish live in rock pools.		
Rock pools are always very cold.		

END OF TEST

/ 6

There are **5 questions**.
Give yourself **10 minutes** to read the text and answer them.

The Vikings

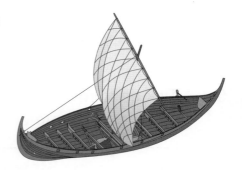

The Vikings were a group of people who came from the north of Europe. They lived around 1000 years ago.

Great explorers

Many Vikings travelled to other countries to explore and trade. They were very good at sailing, which helped them to travel a long way.

Vikings often sailed in boats called longships, which looked a bit like big canoes. These ships were wooden and could carry up to 60 people.

Fierce warriors

Vikings also went to other countries to steal from towns, villages and churches. Lots of people were terrified of them. They attacked and killed people, and burned buildings to the ground.

The Vikings in Britain

The Vikings attacked Britain and tried to take it over. Some Viking families moved to Britain to start a new life. They settled in towns and villages and built their own houses. Many of them became farmers.

Even though some left, lots of Vikings stayed in Britain. Many British people alive today are their distant relatives.

1. What were the Vikings very good at?

Tick **one** box.

sailing ☐

running ☐

climbing ☐

hunting ☐

1 mark

2. What was the name of the boats that the Vikings often used?

....

1 mark

3. Look at the section called *Fierce warriors*.

Find and **copy one** word that shows that people found the Vikings scary.

....

1 mark

4. What did many Vikings become when they came
    to Britain?

    ....

5. Tick each row to show whether each statement about
    the Vikings is **true** or **false**.

Statement	True	False
They explored other countries.		
They came from north Africa.		
They sailed in small canoes.		
Many of them moved to Britain.		

END OF TEST

/ 6

There are **5 questions**.
Give yourself **10 minutes** to read the text and answer them.

The Toy Shop

Ben entered the busy shop with his mum and gasped with excitement. His mum had said that this was the largest toy shop in the city and now he believed her. It was enormous!

To his right were boxes and boxes of dolls, teddy bears and cuddly toys. To his left there were rails full of dressing up costumes. Ben loved dressing up and couldn't wait to try them on.

Ben squeezed through the crowd to reach the costumes. They had everything — pirates, gorillas, princesses, astronauts... He put on the helmet from a robot costume and turned to show his mum. But she wasn't there! Ben took the helmet off and looked around. He couldn't see her. His heart started to beat very fast.

Suddenly, he saw a flash of his mum's blue coat. Ben pushed his way over and pulled at the lady's sleeve. But when she turned around, he realised that she wasn't his mum.

"Oh, I'm sorry," said Ben. He didn't know what to do, and he felt like bursting into tears. Just then, he felt a hand on his shoulder. It was his mum! He threw his arms around her.

"There you are!" cried his mum, holding him tightly. "You had me worried. I know you're excited, but stay close to me next time!"

1. What did Ben see on his left when he went into the toy shop?

....

2. Ben tried on a helmet in the toy shop.

Which costume was it from?

Tick **one** box.

a pirate costume ☐

an astronaut costume ☐

a gorilla costume ☐

a robot costume ☐

3. How do you know that Ben was happy to see his mum again?

....

....

4. a) Think about the story you have just read.
   If Ben went shopping with his mum again, how do
   you think Ben would act differently?

   ....

   b) How can you tell?

   ....

   ....

5. Number these events in the order in
   which they happened in the story.

   The first one has been done for you.

   Ben realised he had lost his mum.   ☐

   Ben and his mum went into a toy shop.   1

   Ben's mum found him.   ☐

   Ben went to look at the costumes.   ☐

   Ben thought a stranger was his mum.   ☐

   END OF TEST   / 6

There are **5 questions**.
Give yourself **10 minutes** to read the text and answer them.

On Top of the World

Mount Everest is the highest mountain in the world. It is more than six times the height of Britain's tallest mountain. A lot of people have tried to climb to the top of Mount Everest. Many have succeeded, but many others have failed.

A dangerous place

People have to climb over snow, ice and rocks to get to the top of Everest. This can be unsafe. For example, you can be hit by falling rocks and ice. The temperature and powerful winds on Everest make it even more dangerous to climb. The weather can change from good to bad very quickly, so climbers need to be very well prepared.

The long climb

The trip up and down Mount Everest usually takes around two months. There is nowhere to stay on the mountain, so climbers sleep in tents. Most people climb with guides called Sherpas. They live near Mount Everest and know how to climb the mountain safely.

Reaching the top

The first people to climb to the top of Mount Everest were Edmund Hillary from New Zealand and Tenzing Norgay, who was a Sherpa from Nepal. They reached the top in 1953. Since then, thousands of people from all over the world have also completed the climb.

1. Mount Everest is a dangerous place.
    One reason for this is that...

                                                    Tick **one** box.

        you might get hit by falling rocks.   ☐

        there are lots of people climbing it.   ☐

        the weather never changes.   ☐

        climbers aren't well prepared.   ☐

                                                    _____
                                                    1 mark

2. *The temperature and powerful winds on Everest...*

    What does the word *powerful* mean in this sentence?

                        Tick **one** box.

        light   ☐

        scary   ☐

        weak   ☐

        strong   ☐

                                                    _____
                                                    1 mark

3. Look at the section called *The long climb*.

    How long does it normally take to climb up and down
    Mount Everest?

    ....

                                                    _____
                                                    1 mark

4. Which country was Edmund Hillary from?

    ....

    _____
    1 mark

5. Tick each row to show whether each statement about
    Mount Everest is **true** or **false**.

Statement	True	False
It is easy to get to the top.		
It is very cold there.		
Sherpas help people get to the top.		
No-one reached the top before 1953.		

_____
2 marks

END OF TEST

/ 6

There are **5 questions**.
Give yourself **10 minutes** to read the text and answer them.

The Owl and the Snake

There was once an owl who lived in a forest with her baby owlet. Owl was kind to everyone, except for the snake who lived near her nest. Owl's friends had told her that all snakes were evil. So she was cruel to Snake and chased him away whenever he came near.

One night, Owl woke up to great panic in the forest. A blanket of smoke lay over the trees and all the animals stared in fright. A fire!

Together, the animals began to run. But as Owl was about to leave, she realised Owlet was stuck in a hole inside their tree. The hole was so small that Owl couldn't reach him. Owl screeched in panic and began to cry.

"Please, Mr Robin, just a minute!" she called out to her fleeing friends. "Miss Mouse, wait, I need your help!"

But all of her friends ignored her. They were too afraid to stay and help. Only Snake listened to Owl's shouts and paused to wriggle inside the tree. In an instant he had reappeared, carrying Owlet gently in his mouth. Together, they got out of the forest to safety.

"Oh *thank* you, Snake!" hooted Owl. "That was so kind. I'm sorry, I was wrong to believe what my friends told me about you." And from that day on, Owl never judged others without knowing them first.

1. Draw lines to match each character to their actions in the story.

Character	Action
Owl	chased Snake away
Mr Robin	got stuck inside a tree
Owlet	ignored his friend

1 mark

2. What did Owl's friends tell her about snakes?

....

1 mark

3. Why couldn't Owl get into the hole inside the tree?

....

1 mark

4. How can you tell that Owl was scared when Owlet was stuck inside the tree? Give **two** ways.

1) ....

2) ....

2 marks

5. Number these events in the order in which they happened in the story.

    The first one has been done for you.

    Owl asked her friends for help.   ☐

    Owl thanked Snake.   ☐

    Snake rescued Owlet.   ☐

    A fire began in the forest.   ☐

    Owl was cruel to Snake.   1

1 mark

END OF TEST

/ 6

There are **6 questions**.
Give yourself **10 minutes** to read the text and answer them.

Friends

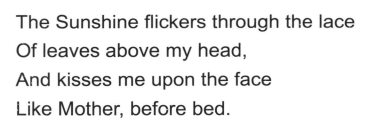

How good to lie a little while
And look up through the tree!
The Sky is like a kind big smile
Bent sweetly over me.

The Sunshine flickers through the lace
Of leaves above my head,
And kisses me upon the face
Like Mother, before bed.

The Wind comes stealing o'er* the grass
To whisper pretty things;
And though I cannot see him pass,
I feel his careful wings.

by Abbie Farwell Brown

*o'er = over

1. The person in the poem thinks it's good to lie down and...

Tick **one** box.

smile at the tree. ☐

look up through the tree. ☐

bend over the tree. ☐

be kind to the tree. ☐

1 mark

2. **Find** and **copy two** words that show the sky is friendly.

1) ....

2) ....

1 mark

3. Who kisses the person in the poem before they go to bed?

....

1 mark

4. What does the wind blow over to reach the person in the poem?

....

5. *To whisper pretty things*

What does *whisper* mean in this sentence?

Tick **one** box.

to make a musical sound	☐
to make a quiet sound	☐
to make a loud sound	☐
to make an angry sound	☐

1 mark

6. Why does the person in the poem like lying on the ground?

Tick **one** box.

because it's more comfortable than bed	☐
because it's a good place to read	☐
because they like being near nature	☐
because there is no wind	☐

1 mark

END OF TEST

/ 6

End of Set B: Scoresheet

You've finished a full set of tests — well done!

Put your scores in here
to see how you're doing...

	Score	
Test 1		/6
Test 2		/6
Test 3		/6
Test 4		/6
Test 5		/6
Test 6		/6
Total		**/36**

... then look up your total score to see what's next:

0 – 12	You might need some **more practice**. Ask an adult to help, then try the tests again.
13 – 24	**Read** back over your **wrong** answers to see **why** they were wrong. Then try the **next set** of tests.
25 – 36	Well done! Try to beat your score on the **next set** of tests.

But first... bend your brain round this:

What follows you everywhere? Your...

S _____ _____ _____ **D** _____ _____ **W** _____

There are **5 questions**.
Give yourself **10 minutes** to read the text and answer them.

Guinea Pigs

The first guinea pigs lived in the wild in South America, where some still live today. Since then, guinea pigs have become popular pets.

Food

Guinea pigs mainly eat hay and fresh grass. Some vegetables, like broccoli, are good snacks. It's also important to feed your guinea pig special pellets every day. These contain vitamins that help them to stay healthy. You wouldn't want your guinea pig to become poorly!

Habitat

It's good to have more than one guinea pig because they like to have company. They will need somewhere safe to sleep, such as a hutch. Make sure they always have clean, warm bedding and fresh water.

Behaviour

Like cats, guinea pigs purr when they are happy. You might also hear them make a squeaking sound. This often happens when they see their owner or when it's feeding time.

Building a good relationship

Although it may be nervous at first, a guinea pig will often be more comfortable with you if you stroke it. Feeding it a tasty treat at the same time will also help it to trust you.

1. Where did the first guinea pigs live?

....

2. *These contain vitamins that help them to stay healthy.*

What does the word *healthy* mean in this sentence?

Tick **one** box.

tired ☐

well ☐

full ☐

sad ☐

3. Why might a guinea pig squeak? Give **two** reasons.

1) ....

2) ....

4.   Stroking a guinea pig can make it more...

Tick **one** box.

nervous with you. ☐

comfortable with you. ☐

angry with you. ☐

frightened of you. ☐

5.   Tick each row to show whether each statement about guinea pigs is **true** or **false**.

Statement	True	False
They don't like to have company.		
Some guinea pigs live in the wild.		
They are unpopular pets.		
They eat hay and fresh grass.		

2 marks

END OF TEST

/ 6

There are **5 questions**.
Give yourself **10 minutes** to read the text and answer them.

The Lady of Stavoren

Long ago, in a town called Stavoren, there was once a beautiful harbour. Many ships came to the harbour to buy and sell things. This made the people who lived in Stavoren rich and happy.

By the harbour lived a very rich lady. But the lady was greedy and wasn't happy with the money that she had. One day, she asked the town's best sailor to bring her the most precious thing in the world.

For months the lady waited. She dreamed of jewels as big as eggs and chests filled with gold. Finally, the sailor's ship returned and the lady ran on board.

"Well, where is it?" she demanded. "What did you find?"

The sailor pointed to a pile of wheat that was heaped on the deck.

"Without wheat, we couldn't make bread," he explained. "And without bread, we would starve. It's the most precious thing in the world."

The lady stormed off the ship and ordered the wheat to be tipped into the harbour. Over the next few weeks, the wheat grew up from the harbour floor and blocked the harbour off from the sea. Without its harbour, Stavoren became poor. The lady's greed had ruined the town and the lady herself lost everything.

43

1. How long did the lady wait for the ship to come back?

....

1 mark

2. What did the lady dream about while she was waiting? Give **two** things.

1) ....

2) ....

1 mark

3. Why did the sailor think that wheat was the most precious thing in the world?

Tick **one** box.

it is worth a lot of money ☐

it is the tastiest food in the world ☐

it stops people from starving ☐

it is rare ☐

1 mark

4. How can you tell that the lady was angry about the wheat? Give **two** ways.

1) ....

    ....

2) ....

    ....

2 marks

5. Number these events in the order in which they happened in the story.

    The first one has been done for you.

    The lady waited for the sailor to return. $\boxed{1}$

    The wheat was tipped into the harbour. $\boxed{}$

    The sailor showed the lady the wheat. $\boxed{}$

    Stavoren became poor. $\boxed{}$

1 mark

END OF TEST $\boxed{ / 6}$

There are **5 questions**.
Give yourself **10 minutes** to read the text and answer them.

April Fool

Harrison woke up and turned over his calendar excitedly. Today was the first day of April. Yesterday, Mr Shaw had taught them all about April Fool's Day and how people played tricks on each other. Harrison had gone home and thought up a brilliant plan of his own.

Harrison got dressed and crept quietly into the garage, trying not to wake up his sister Katie. He went over to a huge cardboard box, emptied it carefully, then slipped back inside the house. But he didn't notice that his mum was watching him from the kitchen window...

Later that day, Harrison's mum saw him fetch the cardboard box and put it outside the front door. She smiled to herself as she watched him giggle, ring the doorbell, then quickly climb inside the box.

Katie opened the door and looked at the parcel in confusion.

"April Fool!" yelled Harrison, leaping up out of the box and causing Katie to scream and jump backwards.

"April Fool to you, too!" cried his mum, appearing with a water pistol. "Bad luck, Harrison, I always know when you're up to something!"

Harrison ducked and laughed as a jet of water flew towards him. He enjoyed his mum's trick, even if he had ended up being an April Fool!

1. What date does this story take place on?

Tick **one** box.

1st April ☐

2nd April ☐

4th April ☐

30th April ☐

_____

1 mark

2. Where did Harrison find the cardboard box?

....

_____

1 mark

3. Look at the paragraph beginning *Later that day,
Harrison's mum saw him fetch the cardboard box...*

Find and **copy one** word that means the same as
laugh.

....

_____

1 mark

4.   Where did Harrison hide to surprise Katie?

                                              Tick **one** box.

                in the garage   ☐

                under his bed   ☐

                in the kitchen   ☐

                outside the front door   ☐

                                                    ———————
                                                    1 mark

5.   How can you tell that Katie was surprised when
       Harrison jumped out of the box? Give **two** ways.

       1) ....

       2) ....
                                                    ———————
                                                    2 marks

END OF TEST   ┌──────────┐
                                       │   / 6 │
                                       └──────────┘

There are **5 questions**.
Give yourself **10 minutes** to read the text and answer them.

The Story Behind Paper

Most of us come into contact with paper every day. But have you ever stopped to wonder where it comes from or how it's made?

From wood to paper

Most paper is made from trees. Trees are cut down and taken to a factory. They are then chopped into small pieces, boiled and rolled out into sheets of paper. The paper is dried and wound into huge rolls, ready to be transported out of the factory.

Different types of paper

Paper can be used to make a variety of products, not just the obvious items like books and magazines. Tissues, wallpaper, bandages, teabags — the list is endless! Paper is even used to make art. Some artists fold or cut paper to make impressive sculptures.

Paper and the environment

Cutting down lots of trees can be harmful to the environment. Every day, over two million trees are cut down for paper. Many people now try to use products, such as newspapers and toilet paper, which have been made from re-used paper. You can do your own bit to help by re-using paper at home. For example, you could use scrap paper to draw or write on.

1.　Where are the trees taken after they are cut down?

....

━━━━━
1 mark

2.　Look at the section called *From wood to paper.*

Find and **copy one** word that means the same as *big*.

....

━━━━━
1 mark

3.　Why do people use products made from re-used paper?

Tick **one** box.

to save money　　　　☐

to save newspapers　☐

to save time　　　　 ☐

to save trees　　　　 ☐

━━━━━
1 mark

4. What does the text say you could use to draw or write on?

....

5. Tick each row to show whether each statement about paper is **true** or **false**.

Statement	True	False
Paper is usually made from trees.		
We don't use paper very often.		
Paper doesn't have many uses.		
Some people make sculptures out of paper.		

2 marks

END OF TEST

/ 6

There are **5 questions**.
Give yourself **10 minutes** to read the text and answer them.

Scamper the Mouse

Scamper let out an excited squeak. Alice had forgotten to close her cage! Today, after waiting all her life, she was finally going outside.

For as long as Scamper could remember, the birds outside the window had sung songs to her about the outside world. The trees, the fields, the flowers... Scamper longed to see them for herself. But Alice thought it was too dangerous and wouldn't let Scamper go.

Scamper raced to the front door and darted through the cat flap. Her whiskers quivered happily as she decided which delicious smell to follow first. She set off across the road, gazing around in wonder. She had just paused to sniff some flowers, when a loud cry rang out.

"A mouse! A mouse in my garden! Oh, somebody get it, quickly!"

Alice's neighbour, Mrs Pebbles, was charging towards Scamper, flapping her arms and stomping her feet. Terrified, Scamper tried to dash back over the road, but two hands quickly snatched her up.

The tip of Scamper's nose trembled with fright as the fingers holding her parted. In the light, Alice's face appeared. What a relief! Alice apologised to Mrs Pebbles, then carried Scamper gently indoors.

Back inside, Scamper snuggled into her straw, safe and sound. Happy to be home, she drifted off into a contented sleep.

1. Who told Scamper about the outside world?

Tick **one** box.

the trees ☐

Alice ☐

the flowers ☐

the birds ☐

_____

1 mark

2. In the story, Mrs Pebbles let out a *loud cry*.

This means that she let out...

Tick **one** box.

a long laugh. ☐

a big scream. ☐

a deep sigh. ☐

a noisy whisper. ☐

_____

1 mark

3. Who picked up Scamper as she tried to run back home?

....

_____

1 mark

4. Draw lines to match each character to their actions in the story.

Character	Description
Alice	went to explore outside
Scamper	forgot to shut the cage
Mrs Pebbles	saw a mouse in her garden

1 mark

5. a) Think about the story you have just read.
       If Alice left Scamper's cage open again, what do you think Scamper would do?

       ....

       1 mark

    b) How can you tell?

       ....

       ....

       1 mark

END OF TEST

/ 6

There are **6 questions**.
Give yourself **10 minutes** to read the text and answer them.

A Good Play

We built a ship upon the stairs
All made of the back-bedroom chairs,
And filled it full of sofa pillows
To go a-sailing on the billows*.

We took a saw and several nails,
And water in the nursery pails*;
And Tom said, "Let us also take
An apple and a slice of cake;"—
Which was enough for Tom and me
To go a-sailing on, till tea.

We sailed along for days and days,
And had the very best of plays;
But Tom fell out and hurt his knee,
So there was no one left but me.

by Robert Louis Stevenson

> *billows = large waves
> *pails = buckets

1. Where did the children build the ship?

Tick **one** box.

on the sofa ☐

on the stairs ☐

in the back bedroom ☐

in the nursery ☐

1 mark

2. *We took a saw and several nails*

What does the word *several* mean in this sentence?

Tick **one** box.

short ☐

a few ☐

strong ☐

sharp ☐

1 mark

3. What food did the children take onto the ship?
Give **two** things.

1) ....

2) ....

1 mark

4. **Find** and **copy one** word that shows the children had a good time.

....

1 mark

5. What happened to Tom at the end of the poem?

....

....

1 mark

6. How many children played on the ship?

....

1 mark

END OF TEST

/ 6

End of Set C: Scoresheet

You've finished a full set of tests — well done!

Put your scores in here
to see how you're doing...

	Score	
Test 1		/6
Test 2		/6
Test 3		/6
Test 4		/6
Test 5		/6
Test 6		/6
Total		**/36**

... then look up your total score to see what's next:

0 – 12	You might need some **more practice**. Ask an adult to help, then try the tests again.
13 – 24	**Read** back over your **wrong** answers to see **why** they were wrong. Then have another go.
25 – 36	You've done really well — great work!

But first... bend your brain round this:

Rearrange the letters below to make a colour...

E R E G N _ _ _ _ _ _

Answers

There are 5 different elements which can be assessed
in the Key Stage 1 Reading SATs paper.

Throughout the answers, we have indicated in **brackets** which element each
question covers, so you can work out how children are progressing in each area.

The 5 elements can be summarised as follows:

1a:	Draw on knowledge of vocabulary to understand texts.

1b:	Identify / explain key aspects of fiction and non-fiction texts, such as characters, events, titles and information.

1c:	Identify and explain the sequence of events in texts.

1d:	Make inferences from the text.

1e:	Predict what might happen on the basis of what has been read so far.

Set A

Test 1 — Pages 2-4

1. 1 mark
   worried
   (1b)

2. 1 mark
   to make posters
   (1b)

3. 1 mark
   put up Aditi's posters.
   (1b)

4. 1 mark for all 4 correct
   Mum and Aditi put up some posters. — 2
   Aditi's cat went missing. — 1
   The man thought he knew where Tibbles was. — 3
   Mum and Aditi went to the man's house. — 4
   (1c)

5. 1 mark for one correct
   2 marks for two correct
   She jumped into Aditi's arms.
   She purred happily.
   (1d)

Answers

Test 2 — Pages 5-7

1. 1 mark

planning a birthday party
(1b)

2. 1 mark

decide
(1a)

3. 1 mark

your closest friends
(1b)

4. 1 mark for all 4 correct

Choose how many people to invite.
— 1
Organise activities for your guests.
— 3
Make sure you have lots of prizes. — 4
Choose where you will have
the party. — 2
(1c)

5. 1 mark for 3 correct
2 marks for all 4 correct

Large parties should be held
in a small place. — False
Restaurants don't provide any food.
— False
Activities will entertain
your guests. — True
Birthday parties can be fun for family
and friends. — True
(1b)

Test 3 — Pages 8-10

1. 1 mark

He had fallen into a pit.
(1b)

2. 1 mark

He would get sunburnt.
(1b)

3. 1 mark

looked
(1a)

4. 1 mark for one correct
2 marks for two correct

He jumped quickly into the hole.
He pushed Lucky Bob aside.
(1d)

5. 1 mark for all 3 correct

Lucky Bob left Captain Billhook
a note. — 4
Fearless Fabio was chased up a
tree. — 1
Lucky Bob hit Captain Billhook. — 3
Lucky Bob found the treasure. — 2
(1c)

Test 4 — Pages 11-13

1. 1 mark

a week
(1b)

2. 1 mark

Sharon — the riding instructor
Martin — Felix's cousin
Beth — the pony that Felix rode
(1b)

Answers

3. 1 mark

Martin wanted to ride a bigger pony.
(1d)

4. 1 mark

walk forward
(1b)

5. a) 1 mark for a sensible answer, e.g.

He wouldn't try to ride a big horse.
(1e)

b) 1 mark for a sensible answer, e.g.

He felt more comfortable on Shelly.
(1e)

Test 5 — Pages 14-16

1. 1 mark

strong fabric
(1b)

2. 1 mark

by tilting their bodies
(1b)

3. 1 mark

risky
(1a)

4. 1 mark

They have a perfect view of the world below them.
(1d)

5. 1 mark for 3 correct
2 marks for all 4 correct

The longest flight ever is 45 miles.
— False
They have no engines. — True
They are controlled by their pilots.
— True.
They are made out of paper.
— False
(1b)

Test 6 — Pages 17-19

1. 1 mark

it's caring
(1b)

2. 1 mark

home
(1a)

3. 1 mark

at the same speed as the child.
(1d)

4. 1 mark for 2 of the following

legs
feet
wings
(1b)

5. 1 mark

above a roof
(1b)

6. 1 mark

following the child
(1d)

Answers

Scoresheet Question — Page 20
SNAKE

Set B

Test 1 — Pages 21-23

1. 1 mark

by the sea
(1b)

2. 1 mark

discover
(1a)

3. 1 mark

so they don't get washed away
(1b)

4. 1 mark

the sea
(1b)

5. 1 mark for 3 correct
2 marks for all 4 correct

Not many different animals live in rock pools. — False
Rock pools are filled with seawater. — True
Some small fish live in rock pools. — True
Rock pools are always very cold. — False
(1b)

Test 2 — Pages 24-26

1. 1 mark

sailing
(1b)

2. 1 mark

longships
(1b)

3. 1 mark

terrified
(1a)

4. 1 mark

farmers
(1b)

5. 1 mark for 3 correct
2 marks for all 4 correct

They explored other countries. — True
They came from north Africa. — False
They sailed in small canoes. — False
Many of them moved to Britain. — True
(1b)

Test 3 — Pages 27-29

1. 1 mark

dressing up costumes
(1b)

2. 1 mark

a robot costume
(1b)

3. 1 mark

He threw his arms around her.
(1d)

Answers

4. a) 1 mark for any sensible answer, e.g.

He would stay close to his mum.
(1e)

b) 1 mark for any sensible answer, e.g.

He was scared when he lost her.
(1e)

5. 1 mark for all 4 correct

Ben realised he had lost his mum. — 3
Ben and his mum went into a toy shop. — 1
Ben's mum found him. — 5
Ben went to look at the costumes. — 2
Ben thought a stranger was his mum. — 4
(1c)

Test 4 — Pages 30-32

1. 1 mark

you might get hit by falling rocks.
(1b)

2. 1 mark

strong
(1a)

3. 1 mark

around 2 months
(1b)

4. 1 mark

New Zealand
(1b)

5. 1 mark for 3 correct
2 marks for all 4 correct

It is easy to get to the top. — False
It is very cold there. — True
Sherpas help people get to the top. — True
No-one reached the top before 1953. — True
(1d)

Test 5 — Pages 33-35

1. 1 mark for all 3 correct

Owl — chased Snake away
Mr Robin — ignored his friend
Owlet — got stuck inside a tree
(1b)

2. 1 mark

They are all evil.
(1b)

3. 1 mark

The hole was too small / Owl was too big.
(1b)

4. 1 mark for one correct
2 marks for two correct

She screeched in panic.
She began to cry.
(1d)

5. 1 mark for all 4 correct

Owl asked her friends for help. — 3
Owl thanked Snake. — 5
Snake rescued Owlet. — 4
A fire began in the forest. — 2
Owl was cruel to snake. — 1
(1c)

Answers

Test 6 — Pages 36-38

1. 1 mark

look up through the tree.
(1b)

2. 1 mark for 2 of the following

kind
smile
sweetly
(1a)

3. 1 mark

the person in the poem's mother
(1b)

4. 1 mark

the grass
(1b)

5. 1 mark

to make a quiet sound
(1a)

6. 1 mark

because they like being near nature
(1d)

Scoresheet Question — Page 39
SHADOW

Set C

Test 1 — Pages 40-42

1. 1 mark

South America
(1b)

2. 1 mark

well
(1a)

3. 1 mark for both correct

because it sees its owner
because it's feeding time
(1b)

4. 1 mark

comfortable with you.
(1b)

5. 1 mark for 3 correct
2 marks for all 4 correct

They don't like to have company.
— False
Some guinea pigs live in the wild.
— True
They are unpopular pets. — False
They eat hay and fresh grass. — True
(1b)

Test 2 — Pages 43-45

1. 1 mark

months
(1b)

2. 1 mark for both correct

jewels as big as eggs
chests filled with gold
(1b)

3. 1 mark

it stops people from starving
(1b)

Answers

4. 1 mark for one correct
2 marks for both correct

She stormed off the ship.
She ordered the wheat to be tipped into the harbour.
(1d)

5. 1 mark for all 3 correct

The lady waited for the sailor to return.
— 1
The wheat was tipped into the harbour.
— 3
The sailor showed the lady the wheat.
— 2
Stavoren became poor. — 4
(1c)

Test 3 — Pages 46-48

1. 1 mark

1st April
(1b)

2. 1 mark

in the garage
(1b)

3. 1 mark

giggle
(1a)

4. 1 mark

outside the front door
(1b)

5. 1 mark for one correct
2 marks for two correct

She screamed.
She jumped backwards.
(1d)

Test 4 — Pages 49-51

1. 1 mark

a factory
(1b)

2. 1 mark

huge
(1a)

3. 1 mark

to save trees
(1d)

4. 1 mark

scrap paper
(1b)

5. 1 mark for 3 correct
2 marks for all 4 correct

Paper is usually made from trees.
— True
We don't use paper very often.
— False
Paper doesn't have many uses.
— False
Some people make sculptures out of paper. — True
(1b)

Answers

Test 5 — Pages 52-54

1. 1 mark

the birds
(1b)

2. 1 mark

a big scream.
(1a)

3. 1 mark

Alice
(1d)

4. 1 mark for all 3 correct

Alice — forgot to shut the cage
Scamper — went to explore outside
Mrs Pebbles — saw a mouse in her garden
(1b)

5. a) 1 mark for any sensible answer, e.g.

She would stay inside the cage.
(1e)

b) 1 mark for any sensible answer, e.g.

It was scary outside and she was happy to be back in her cage.
(1e)

Test 6 — Pages 55-57

1. 1 mark

on the stairs
(1b)

2. 1 mark

a few
(1a)

3. 1 mark for both correct

an apple
a slice of cake
(1b)

4. 1 mark

best
(1d)

5. 1 mark

He fell out of the ship and hurt his knee.
(1b)

6. 1 mark

two
(1d)

Scoresheet Question — Page 58
GREEN

EXPR11